The Triumphant *Tale* of Tunie

Once upon a time, in a sleepy township neighboring San Pablo Bay in Northern California there breathed a household of mice named the River Biscuit Family. San Rafael and Santa Rosa River Biscuit had been high school sweethearts. More notably, they were well-intentioned mice who, with reliance and grace, surrendered their lives to God. Living in Parchester Village, they together nurtured four little bucks, christened so perfectly as San Rafael, San Mateo, San Francisco, and San Diego. Little San Rafael, later known as Rafie, was the first-born of the four mice.

The Triumphant *Tale of Tunie*

A Little Mouse, with Big Dreams, and the Heart of Love

Joseph M. Silveira Ed.D.

LifeRich Publishing is a registered trademark of The Reader's Digest Association, Inc.

LifeRich Publishing books may be ordered through booksellers or by contacting:

LifeRich Publishing
1151 W. 2nd St
Bloomington IN 47403
www.liferichpublishing.com
844-686-9607

ISBN: 978-1-4897-5298-7 (sc)
ISBN: 978-1-4897-5297-0 (hc)
ISBN: 978-1-4897-5296-3 (e)

Library of Congress Control Number: 2025926777

Print information available on the last page.

LifeRich Publishing rev. date: 02/25/2026

LifeRich
PUBLISHING®

Upon graduating from Bishop Mouse High School, Rafie received a full-drive scholarship, on a granary wagon, to Magnificent Mouse University. Although he was a standout football defensive corner-back in the North Coast Section, Rafie was lauded as a track star with the fastest 100-meter time and longest recorded jump in Mouse League high school history. At his sendoff celebration from home, and amongst his much-loved family and friends Grandmamma Mouse exclaimed, "God above has guided our love."

Realizing his degree in Liberal Arts from Magnificent Mouse University, Rafie then entered Mount Mousie University's Teaching Credential Program. This phase of life proved unmatched for Rafie, as this is where he met, courted, and wed the mouse of his life, Santa Rita. Rafie and Rita ultimately settled in the pastoral knolls of Franklin Canyon, near Highway 4 amid the towns of Pinole, and Martinez not far from Parchester Village.

Rafie and Rita assembled their lives on a glorious hilltop overlooking San Pablo Bay with a picture-perfect view of Mount Mousetrap Tamalpais. Their abode sat atop the Muir Ranch's oak-studded hillsides where coats of lupine and California poppy, wild oats, rye grass, and yellow mustard undulated to the whistling winds of springtime. Located in a century-old cello, their joyful home was buoyed in a nook of the great room of Muir Manor.

On the eve of their first anniversary, Mr. and Mrs. River Biscuit fondly reminisced about their wedding day at Saint Michael-Mice College as they sipped nectar water, nipped dark chocolate, and danced to the melodies of their favorite rock group, U2-RA Mouse. At the end of the evening Rafie proclaimed to Rita, "God above has blessed our love."

However, the happiest day of their lifecycle occurred when Rita gave birth to a brood of seven mice at the lowermost level of the cello. Once Mommy Mouse was strong and healthy, she and the proud papa fashioned the names of their seven little ones, so impeccably as San Ramon, San Miguel, Santa Anna, San Jose, Santa Maria, and San Antonio. Hitherto, the River Biscuits struggled all day to treasure a name for the tiniest and feeblest mouse of them all.

"Mommy, this little one deserves a very special name," said Papa Rafie. "Let's not force the bloom, and let's pray for providence." Suddenly, the manor's large French doors opened to the jovial sounds of an enormous, brassy-voiced man befittingly named, Boomer.

"Boomer, we were expecting you to arrive tomorrow," Mrs. Muir rang out. "So we had not a moment's gander of preparation to remove the cello from its perch adjacent to the bay window."

"Not to fret," cried Boomer. "The honor of removing this cello from its roost is well beyond the gift of tuning it up, especially after all these muffled years."

Upon clutching the cello, Boomer unexpectedly slipped and tumbled to the floor, while Mrs. Muir's fine porcelain rattled in the glass dining cabinet, like the roar from a lightning strike, beside the great room's cedar wall.

"Are you okay, Mr. Boomer?" squealed Mrs. Muir.

"Does the Pope like Pici pasta?" Boomer burst out. "Of course, I am well; my solitary concern at this moment rests with your family's priceless heirloom and, thankfully, all is well!"

Little did Boomer know that, inside the cello, San Rafael and Santa Rita's dwelling and offspring were sprinkled about like fallen oats from a gunny sack. Thankfully, the doting parents located all the children soon thereafter, with the exception of the littlest one, who was dangling by his *tail* on an exiled chord in the epicenter of the cello.

"My beloved, my beloved, my beloved…" Papa Rafie sputtered as Boomer tweaked the cello. "Oh, little one, we have not named you yet, but thankfully God above has sheltered your adorable siblings and you too, our littlest love."

Although the teeny mouse sustained many bumps and bruises from the fall, Rafie considered the little one to be intact, but, after further notice, he and Mama Rita confirmed that their precious droplet of spirit had severed several tendons in his left foot.

That evening, the River Biscuits called in Doctor Wise-Cracker to examine the whole family and, before long, the good doctor established that everyone checked out just fine, except for Mama Rita Mouse, and the littlest one of them all. In the plunge, Mama Rita had fractured two ribs, yet she never shilly-shallied in devoting her attention to her husband and pocket-sized mice. Early that morning and late into the evening, Mama Mouse sang her favorite melody to her coterie. "God above has shared our love." While Mama Rita nursed the smallest one back to health, a day arose when Papa and Mama befittingly named the little sprout "San Tune," in honor of their family's episode in the cello.

Unfortunately, after a sudden illness and serious complications a month to the date after the cartwheel chaos, sustained in the cello, Mommy Mouse passed on from complications due to walking pneumonia. Papa Mouse would never marry again, and the townsfolk observed him placing newly gathered poppies at the gravesite of his lovely departed wife each Sunday.

Tunie grew up like most mice in his neighborhood. Though he was well-adjusted, he was developmentally delayed in walking. Initially, Tunie received an individualized mouse-education plan at school, and, although he could run and play with the best of his hilltop chums, he had a noticeable hitch in his step that had him strutting around like San George Jefferson.

That didn't break Tunie's spirit though! After many years of physical therapy, mice-ometrics, and fitness, Tunie could run with the best of the mice on the hilltop. In high school, he followed in his father's footprints and later became a celebrated mouse student-athlete at Magnificent Mouse University. There, Tunie developed into an All-American Mouse, and even eclipsed his father's long-standing record in the 100-meter dash.

Upon graduating from Magnificent Mouse University, Tunie was invited to participate in the Mouse Olympic Games in Athens, Greece. Amongst the multitude and with his loved ones and close friends by his side, Tunie mounted the starting blocks eager to participate in the 100-meter dash. Papa mouse mimed from a distance, "God above has graced you, *our* love."

Tunie was *triumphant* in achieving two gold medals at the Mouse Olympic Games, one in the 100-meter dash and one in the long jump. As Tunie River Biscuit stood at the winner's podium in anticipation of his country's national anthem, his father and siblings gazed favorably and stood humbly.

Feeling patriotic at that very instant, Tunie looked to the heavens and thanked God so gently for a life that his parents, and especially his mother, so completely gave to him. Tunie's heart welled up with emotions. At that moment, for the first time in many years, he could miraculously, although faintly hear his mother's lovely voice as she divinely sang, "God above is love."

www.ingramcontent.com/pod-product-compliance
Lightning Source LLC
Chambersburg PA
CBHW042146240326
41723CB00013B/607